Published by Crane Hill Publishers
First edition, first printing, October 1996
Printed in South Korea

A portion of the proceeds from the sale of this book will be donated to
The Breast Cancer Research Foundation of Alabama.

Library of Congress Cataloging-in-Publication Data

Springer, Melissa.
A tribe of warrior women / Melissa Springer.
p. cm.
ISBN: 1-57587-049-5
1. Breast — Cancer — Patients — Alabama — Pictorial works. I. Title
RC280.B8S64 1996
362.1'99449 — dc20 96-7083
CIP

Crane Hill Publishers
2923 Crescent Avenue
Birmingham, Alabama 35209

Carol Dixon
1955-1996

This book is dedicated to my friend Carol Dixon. She was a woman of courage, purity of heart, kindness, and unrelenting loyalty to her family and friends. During the making of this project, Carol knew that because her ovarian cancer had recurred, she had little time left to live.

Carol was my teacher. She taught me about the utter joy of life and she pointed the way to a good and generous death that one day I will receive. She is the purest of warriors and still watches over us. She whispers into my ear and into yours, "Go forth."

I depart as air ...
I bequeath myself to the dirt to
grow from the grass I love,
If you want me again look for
me under your bootsoles.

You will hardly know who I am
or what I mean,
But I shall be good health to
you nevertheless,
And filter and fibre your blood.

Failing to fetch me at first keep
encouraged,
Missing me one place search
another,
I stop some where waiting
for you.

Walt Whitman
"Song of Myself"

acknowledgements

I owe many people my gratitude and thanks for their generous support during the making of the photo-essay for the traveling exhibition and this book. To my sweet husband, Steve Millburg, for creating domestic bliss. To my children, Taylor and Paul Rogers, the first to teach me about bliss. And to Trish Honea-Fleming for reminding me to use it. To Madeline Harris, RN, MSN, OCN, for her vision and determination to bring this project into being. To Ellen, Bobby, Scott, Norma, and the Crane Hill staff for their dedication and enthusiasm. To Charles Collins; Albert LoBuglio, MD; the UAB Comprehensive Cancer Center; Kirklin Clinic; Lindsey Trammell, RN, MSN, OCN; Janis Zeanah; Linda Goodson, RN; Melanie Parker; Carolyn Dunlap; Karen Brown; and Lella Bromberg. To my studio mates Virginia Scruggs, Karen Graffeo, Kim Riegel, Lori Lovoy, Stuart Riddle, and Carolyn Sherer. To the Dixon family, the More group, Dennis and Diane Wammack, Revelle Gwyn, Alan and Susan Rogers, Sonja Rieger, Isie Hanson, Rena Selfe, Douglas Highland, Alyce Head, Ellen Dugan, and Space One Eleven. With gratitude to Art Price for the use of his beautiful painting in the portrait of Sara Orr. With deep respect and love for Lamar Sizemore. To Joe and Ceresa Springer for bringing me to earth. To my siblings, Mikie Snyder, Melinda Springer, and Daryl Springer for being here with me. To Lauren, the Tiny Warrior. A special thank you to the Sokol family for their generous support of this project. And to the women who gave their time and spirits to be part of this project—and to all women with breast cancer.

Melissa Springer

introduction

She is the woman next door, your co-worker, your child's teacher, your best friend, your mother, daughter, sister, aunt, cousin. She could be you.

Walk into any gathering of women, and you are sure to find among them women in the midst of the struggle to overcome breast cancer and women who have engaged in the same struggle and have regained their health. One in eight—given those odds, who among us doesn't know someone who has been besieged by this disease? Who among us while doing what's become our routine breast check or going for our regularly scheduled mammogram hasn't worried or hasn't had a close scare or reason to fear at some time or another?

Not much more than a generation ago most people shied away from saying the word "cancer" out loud as if their silence would keep the disease at a distance. Too often it was assumed that the diagnosis was an automatic death sentence. We knew far less about cancer then than we do now, and as a result of ignorance and fear, folks would whisper that word, sigh and shake their heads in resignation, and hope that by not talking about it, the disease would disappear. For the person who had cancer, this silence often meant feeling isolated and alone.

But as treatments improved and more and more lives were saved and as public awareness of causes, cures, and the importance of early detection increased, the silence and stigmatizing rapidly diminished—*except for women diagnosed with breast cancer.* In a society where women's bodies are worshiped and reviled—and women are all too aware of the breast-obsessed male gaze—the possibility of having to undergo mastectomy as treatment often seems as devastating as the disease itself. Heart-wrenching stories abound of women whose deaths might have been prevented had they agreed to surgery—women who refused surgery for fear of their husbands' or lovers' rejection or for fear that the loss of one or both breasts signified the end of their womanhood. And there are equally painful stories of women who were left feeling inadequate and ashamed after undergoing surgery.

It took a women's revolution—the call for our equality, the claiming of our lives, the naming of our oppression, the recognition of our worth as human beings and not mere objects of desire, and the recognition of our power. It took women's determination to be in charge of our lives in sickness and in health. It took women's consciousness-raising. It took the courage of women who had been diagnosed with the disease and who refused to be silent about their condition to raise the alarm that breast cancer had become epidemic.

And because of women's refusal to be silent and passive in the face of this traumatic, life-threatening disease, there are now support groups, activist organizations, increased funding and research, and an increasing range of better treatments, widespread public information, and grassroots involvement. Today women diagnosed with the disease no longer need to feel isolated and alone. Today women and men wear pink ribbons, October has been declared National Breast Cancer Awareness Month, and across the nation, young and old race or walk for a cure. Today we women are made aware of the importance of early detection, we are better informed about treatment, and we vociferously demand that close attention be paid to uncovering causes as well as cures. And increasingly we women pay ever closer attention to what we can do to change the odds in our favor by monitoring our diets, scrutinizing the environmental and hereditary connections, and demanding more and better woman-friendly care and treatment.

Much has been written about this disease, and it has become the subject of films, plays, dance, performance art, paintings, and sculptures. But none of these expressions is so powerful as the words and works of women—women who have been or are currently engaged in personal struggle to overcome this disease that still claims far too many lives, women sharing their experiences, their feelings, their knowingness. These women proudly bare their chests and exhibit their scars. They are breastless women, one-breasted women, women with prostheses and women who have chosen to go without them, and women whose bodies barely reveal any signs of the assault they've endured. They are women telling their stories—and in the telling, they empower us all.

Each and every member of this sisterhood has a story to tell.

It's common to hear the women who've walked through this valley described as "survivors." But survival can be passive as well as active. And not every member of this sisterhood survives her ordeal. Yet both those who survive and those who don't engage in an epic struggle. From the moment their diagnoses are confirmed, their world is profoundly changed. They are in the center of this struggle, not observers. They are women who have wept and railed and raged—and asked the inevitable "Why me?" questions. They have spent countless hours in quiet reflection and they have spent excruciating hours wrestling with their demons and doubts. They know pain and the smell and taste of fear, and they have come to appreciate the restorative power of love and laughter. They affirm life with a keen awareness that each day is a gift to be prized.

Photojournalist Melissa Springer knows that each and every woman who enters the valley and engages in the struggle with breast cancer becomes a warrior, a woman warrior, a warrior woman—a member of a special tribe. This book is her tribute to those women. It's a book about women's courage. It has many faces—old and young, black and white and a rainbow in between. It's a tribute to the kind of courage that is as much about letting go as it is about holding on—letting go of our vanities and holding on to our humanity. Love fuels this kind of courage: love for others—a mother's desire to be there to nurture her children and watch them grow, love for self, love of life. It can be the courage to believe in some higher power or in choosing not to believe at all. These women warriors need no battle gear, no weapons of war—their power comes from love and laughter, spirit and community.

When Melissa Springer picked up her camera to do these portraits, she was seeking to capture not just each woman's physical presence, but also each woman's courageously joyful spirit, determination, and strength. Melissa talked with them and listened to them with her ears, her eyes, and her heart. What she got as a result is much more than a collection of visually stunning photographs. She got "to the bone" woman-to-woman talk from these 32 members of the tribe—she got each of them to tell what it takes to get through and get over breast cancer, to get through and get over fear.

This is a book by a woman photojournalist in praise of women, a special tribe of women warriors. It's a tribute to all who are members of the tribe. And this book is also a promise to those of us who worry that we may one day be tested by this disease. *A Tribe of Warrior Women* offers the promise that there is hope on the other side—and community along the way.

Marcia Ann Gillespie
Editor in Chief, *Ms.* magazine

A TRIBE OF WARRIOR WOMEN

Patti Bodenhamer
Jerusha Brown
Fannie Crawford-Salter
Evie Ebbinghouse
Jo Fallon
Annette Haislip
Helen Hallman
Lisa Hargrove
Consuello "Connie" J. Harper
Donna Jones
Myra King
Anna Paul Lucy
Geraldine McCaa
Bessie McClinton
Beth McDavid
Sister Mary McGehee, OSB
Nellie McNeil
Anne Nix
Sara Orr
Jane H. Ramsey
Diane Robison
Debbie Sauls
Ruby Self
Kathy Slusher
D.D. Sokol
Priscilla Solomons-Davis
Annie Tate
Marilyn Tillery
Anne Voltz
Sharon Wade
Joe Ann Williamson
Rita Wright

This book is based on an exhibition
originally commissioned
by the
Comprehensive Cancer Center
at the
University of Alabama at Birmingham.

A TRIBE OF *Warrior Women*

AMAZONS
Taken from the Greek word *a-mazos (breastless)*.

A tribe of warrior women
who destroyed one of their breasts
to increase their accuracy
with the javelin and the bow.

Women who knew that to survive,
the aim of the arrow must be precise.
Thousands of women are members
of a fierce tribe of survivors.

These warriors, these breast cancer survivors,
have found weapons to fight and survive
this dreaded disease.

Faith, courage, community, science,
rage, education, and power.

As I was working on this photo-essay, I kept asking myself, *"Who is this for?"* I knew it was an educational tool made to raise awareness about breast cancer, but in my head I kept seeing "her"— a newly diagnosed woman. Every eighth woman will someday be diagnosed with breast cancer. She will be in shock. She will be terrified. I asked each breast cancer survivor I photographed to give "her" some words of comfort. I asked each of them, *"What would you say to her?"* I have included their answers—their message to you.

Melissa Springer

Two thoughts came immediately to Patti when her doctor told her she had cancer: *"Do I have a fighting chance?"* and *"I want see my nine-year-old grow up."* After the biopsy, when the anesthesiologist took off Patti's hair cap, she said, *"Your hair is dark. You're young and strong."* Patti and her daughter, Jordan, now age thirteen, are close. You can see it in their eye contact and in the way they finish each other's thoughts. As Patti lay in bed recovering from the effects of chemotherapy, her eyes focused on the sign in her room that read *"Pray toward heaven, but row toward shore."* Drifting off into sleep, Patti saw Jordan waiting for her on the shore.

Patti Bodenhamer

"Fight like hell and know that you're not alone."

Jerusha is an inmate at Julia Tutwiler Women's Prison. When she was age thirty-four and pregnant, she had a lumpectomy. *"All I cared about was my baby, and she is just fine."* As she talks about cancer, it seems a small thing in her life. Jerusha is HIV positive. She says being sick with cancer and HIV have *"led me to know who Jesus Christ is."* She has *"never claimed"* either disease and has not had a sick day in the last ten years. *"I have asked God to hold me. He has put a shield around me."*

Jerusha Brown

"Let us pray."

"Be strong, keep fighting, and don't give up."

Fannie's new husband says, *"It was love at first sight."* When the romance became serious, Fannie told him about her battle with breast cancer eight years ago. *"I was glad to tell him I had been through something like this and survived. So now he knows that I can survive anything!"* The American Cancer Society recommends women get their first mammogram at age forty. Because of a self-exam, Fannie is a bride at age forty. When she was a single mother in her early thirties, she and her children were terrified with the diagnosis of cancer. Her seven-year-old thought his *"mommy was going to die."* Now as a teenager he gives her the ultimate compliment. *"Mama, you look pretty good for someone who's had breast cancer."*

Fannie Crawford-Salter

When Priscilla found out she had cancer, she thought, *"At least I'll have a spiritual experience."* She was wrong. Instead, she fell into darkness and depression for six months. It was her friends who had the spiritual experience. As she prayed for Priscilla, her close friend Bobbie Gamble felt a voice say, *"I am providing a means for her cure."* Judy Messina, another friend, was always filled with peace when she thought about Priscilla during her illness. They held the faith for Priscilla when she could not. While in her depression, Priscilla made a string of beads to hold when she was taking chemo. She says, *"I had to make the spiritual tangible. I had to hold on to something."*

Priscilla Solomons-Davis

"All shall be well. All shall be well."

The Old Testament
The Old Testament
Woody
The Illustrated Woody Allen Reader
Eudora Welty Photographs
THE MAGIC IMAGE
VanDerZee
PHOTOGRAPHER
ROLLING STONE · THE PHOTOGRAPHS
The Freud/Jung Letters
INVESTMENT
BIKER
ROGERS
ROBERT HUGHES

Evie believes in miracles. She is also good at making them happen. In Birmingham, Alabama, she is known as the Grandmother of PATH, a foundation that gives day shelter to homeless women and children. Many women and children have gathered under her wings. In 1987 Evie was diagnosed with breast cancer. She felt it was a wake-up call to begin her search for healing with love and God. Cancer has given her the opportunity to learn to care for herself, to swim in the currents of miracles, and to celebrate change with gratitude. Every year Evie gives a Butterfly Ball and invites all her friends to celebrate positive changes in their lives. Evie's cancer recurred this year. Plans for the Butterfly Ball are under way.

Evie Ebbinghouse

"Fear not. You are not alone."

I met Jo and her family after I was asked to take a family portrait. As the family gathered to pose, I noticed that Jo was placed in the very center. It was obvious that she is the heart. Later, I found out she has been a survivor for twenty-five years. When her youngest child was four, her doctor told her she would not live very long. So Jo went home to her family and lived each day as if it were her last. She tried *"not to think ahead."* After her tenth survival anniversary, she began to relax a little. When she puts her arms around her grandchildren, you know she takes nothing for granted.

Jo Fallon

"Know that you are loved. God will give you the strength and courage you need."

"Get out, get going, and keep pushing."

A council member of the Poarch Creek Indian Reservation, Helen is skilled in diplomacy, community, and tradition. At age sixteen she quit school to support her eight brothers and sisters. Soon she was "Boss Lady" with the department of agriculture and laughs as she recalls throwing 100-pound sacks of potatoes as fast as a man. In 1990 she was diagnosed with breast cancer. She had a mastectomy on Friday, went home on Monday, and while she was getting her hair done on Tuesday, the hospital was still receiving flowers for her. She credits her survival to the kinship of the reservation. *"I grew up in a community where if somebody killed a hog, everybody got a mess of meat."*

Helen Hallman

As I began work on this project, I wanted to follow a woman through the diagnostic process. In the breast cancer clinic at the University of Alabama at Birmingham, I sat in the examination room with a woman who had just been diagnosed with inflammatory breast cancer: stage four (very advanced). She was terrified, her voice quivered as she told me that her daughter would be seven tomorrow. One year later I am photographing her. She is a survivor! She laughs as she tells me her first thoughts after her grim prognosis. *"I can't die. I have too much junk in my house. My closets and drawers need cleaning out."* Lisa went through aggressive treatment, including a bone marrow transplant and radiation. She is free of cancer. But still she felt something was missing in her life. A fox terrier. So she got one.

Lisa Hargrove

"Find a support group."

OCTOBER
E
Learn
with
us!

Connie is used to conquering irresistible forces. As a schoolteacher in 1958 she had a vision to teach people to help themselves. Connie sought and received help from Governor George Wallace, and she is now the director of OIC (Opportunities Industrialization Center) in Montgomery. Her facility has educated thousands of adults and preschool children. She believes in the power of self. When she was told she had cancer, she said, *"Oh no, Doc, I can't have cancer."* She set to work. She is now free from cancer. *"Surgery and doctors are only tools to help you tap your inner strength."*

Consuello "Connie" J. Harper

"Empower yourself. You hold the destiny."

"Breast cancer is a woman's illness. If this were a man's illness, there would be more monies appropriated." Annette is a direct woman. A schoolteacher for thirty years, Annette asks questions and does her homework. She insisted that her doctor give her all the details. *"This is my body, and I want to know what is going to happen to it."* Because of a diagnosis of lobular cancer, Annette chose to have both breasts removed with immediate reconstruction. She credits her husband with helping her accept the changes in her body. *"I stayed in the hospital for nine days in Atlanta. When we came home and got back in our own house, the first thing we did was make love."*

Annette Haislip

"Go back to work. Stay busy. Go on with your life."

"Hey, I was in your shoes years ago. I fought and won."

After a nine-year remission, Donna's cancer returned last year. Donna went full force: surgery, bone marrow transplant, and radiation. During her hospital stay for the transplant, she and her husband decided to divorce. On that day her white cell count dropped dramatically. She decided *"to do anything to turn it around."* A staff counselor led her through relaxation techniques and positive imaging. The next day her white cell count began to rise. *"I am living proof that your attitude affects the immune system. And I've got the lab work to prove it."* She and her husband are back together. Donna attributes it to a *"miracle of healing"* that occurred between them. They are both enjoying their first grandchild, born seven months after the recurrence.

Donna Jones

Myra's grandfather was a Creek Indian medicine man. You can see the heritage in her beautiful face and strong, clear eyes. She is quiet and observant. A hundred years ago, she would have been a tracker, silently moving through a thick forest following bear. Her husband tells a story about her determination. During her chemo treatments, she still played softball. He watched her hit a grounder to left field. It was a good hit—long and hard. As she rounded second base, he saw her knees start to give, and he knew she was fighting hard to keep going. She went down. But just for a second. His eyes well up as he talks. It is the story of her life.

Myra King

"Let your family be there for you. Don't push them away."

Ms. Lucy comes from a long line of strong, independent women. Her mother and grandmother were widowed at early ages with young children to support. Ms. Lucy says, *"I guess I was just born a fighter."* She is a survivor of fifteen years. She didn't tell her children she was having surgery until it was over. *"They didn't need to know. I was planning on recovering anyway."* She says she has always been the caretaker in the family and is going to keep it that way. But she adds, *"My husband was with me all the way. He supported my choice not to have reconstruction, and that meant a lot to me."*

Anna Paul Lucy

"Get a good doctor and a good hospital."

Geraldine has spent all her life in western Alabama. She is the sole caretaker for her elderly aunt and lives in a trailer behind her aunt's house. Geraldine tends to her relative with grace, love, and thankfulness. In 1994 she had a mastectomy and chemotherapy. She sees this difficulty as just another thing in life to work through. She prays and asks for answers. She always gets a reply. Her two young daughters and husband took care of her during the chemo treatments. Geraldine says, *"Your family has got to take a lot of the load."*

Geraldine McCaa

"Put God in front, and everything will be all right."

Once Bessie's life felt like a shattered dream. She grew up wanting to be an opera singer. Instead, she married and had five beautiful children. In 1986 she was diagnosed with cancer, went through a divorce, and suffered other severe health problems. In 1991 one of her children drowned. Now, at age fifty-four, Bessie radiates peace. When she worked in housekeeping at University Hospital in Birmingham, the nurses often called on her to comfort a depressed patient whom they could not reach. Bessie was never devastated by her diagnosis of cancer. *"I walked proud."* She knew that cancer was not a punishment and that she would be a fighter. But she also adds, *"I wouldn't be caught without God."*

Bessie McClinton

"Wherever you're going, wherever you've been, I've already been there."

Tough women. Women from a strong stock of rural survivors. These sisters, Beth and Nellie, found out at an early age that *"if we stuck together we could survive."* Their grandmother had breast cancer, their mother had breast cancer, and then Nellie's was diagnosed at age fifty-three. Nellie had a mastectomy. Considering the family history, Beth chose to have a bilateral prophylactic mastectomy. Nellie cared for Beth during her recovery. In a quiet moment, discussing her decision to have both breasts removed, Beth asked Nellie, *"If you'd known to do this, wouldn't you?"* Nellie's reply. *"In a second."*

"Be armed with knowledge, family, friends, and love for yourself."

Beth McDavid
Nellie McNeil

Sister Mary knows that the body, mind, and spirit are connected. She learned this on her journey through breast cancer. At age forty-nine, in the year of Jubilee, when all things in our lives need to be put in balance, she was diagnosed with cancer. Sister Mary sees all challenges as paths to greater knowing. Her reaction to having cancer is that *"the whole thing seemed so blessed."* The crisis in her body led her to learn massage as a technique to help in the healing of other bodies. And she adds, *"The work is helping to save my life."*

Sister Mary McGehee, O.S.B.

"This is a transformation. Walk in faith over the water."

Anne's grandchildren call her *"Granny Go Go."* As the wife of the mayor of Fairhope, Anne is involved in every aspect of the community. Everyone in town knows her. You can tell by their greetings that they also love her. She volunteers for the American Cancer Society, organized the support group Bosom Buddies, and is active in the Reach to Recovery program. Her stay in the hospital after her mastectomy lasted less than twenty-four hours. She laughs as she says, *"I couldn't stay away. I might miss something! The worst thing you can do is stay in bed and grieve."* She credits her quick recovery to her friends, her family, and her husband, Jim. *"Bless his heart."*

Anne Nix

"Don't give up. Tell yourself you're going to win!"

Sara is intuitive. It is a skill that has saved her life. In 1990 after a disturbing dream she went to her physician. She was diagnosed with melanoma. She fought hard and recovered. In 1993 she discovered a small lump in her breast. She insisted on a biopsy even though her physician's advice was to "wait and see." She was diagnosed with breast cancer. Sara is a strong woman, active in the world as a writer and mother. She also knows to keep her inner eye on her feelings and body. She believes in angels, and her heart is powerful. Cancer taught her to use her voice, to insist, and to trust herself. She keeps her weapons sharp.

Sara Orr

"Be positive. Let your faith and attitude be a part of your healing."

Jane lives at the end of a country road. Her house is surrounded by cotton fields. Jane walks slowly with the help of a cane. She has been living with multiple sclerosis for fourteen years. When she found out she had MS, her first thought was *"Why me?"* Her second, *"Why not me?"* When diagnosed with breast cancer in 1994, her reaction was the same. Jane is a woman of the land. When crops are destroyed by hail, heat, or pests, you just go on and start planning for next year. Thanks to a yearly mammogram, her cancer was found so early that her doctor has pronounced her *"cured."* Jane believes that *"you play the cards that you're dealt and go on."*

Jane H. Ramsey

"You're going to live. It's not the end of the world."

"Understand the treatment options. Make an informed decision."

Diane has been in the cancer-care field for twenty-five years. She says the hardest part of having cancer was to become the care receiver. Almost overnight she was pushed into the high-risk category for breast cancer when her sister, cousin, and aunt were diagnosed in the same year. Picked up on a mammogram, her breast cancer was labeled premalignant. Since becoming a survivor, her goal as a professional is to tell women that *"they don't have to take off their shoes when they go into a doctor's office and do what they say."* She wants to inform women that a lumpectomy is a viable option. In the United States, 75 percent of women with breast cancer have a lumpectomy. In Mobile, 75 percent have a mastectomy. *"This is unacceptable."*

Diane Robison

Debbie was twenty-nine years old and had a five-year-old, a husband, a great job, and a new house when she heard the words *"you have breast cancer."* During surgery to remove a benign cyst, her doctor discovered some malignant cells. Debbie says the hardest part of having cancer is when you go home and everyone goes back to their own lives. She had many questions and needed to talk to someone who had been there. She asked her doctor about a group, and he said, *"Great idea. You start it. I'll give you a room and an answering machine."* So Debbie created Woman to Woman. This support group has reached hundreds of women since 1988. Many of the charter members stand with her in this photo.

Debbie Sauls

"There is life after breast cancer."

Ruby had a radical mastectomy, with 100 percent of the lymph nodes involved. Cancer recurred three years later, this time in her bones and liver. Through it all she followed the advice of her doctors but says she was *"cradled by the church."* Sometimes she was so sick she *"could not form a prayer,"* but in her community, many hands were pressed together as her name was said. Her doctor feared she was not dealing realistically with the situation because she did not appear concerned. Ruby replied, *"Why be upset? I left it with the Lord. I am not going to worry about it. You worry about it for both of us."* That was thirteen years ago, and the doctor is still worrying.

Ruby Self

"I wish I could take you in my arms."

One night, when Kathy was a child, her father fell off his tractor and it ran over him. Somehow he walked back to the house. She remembers him standing at the back door, a man determined to live. Kathy is her father's daughter, a woman prepared to fight. When she was a welder for the TVA Yellow Creek Nuclear Project, her job was to tear down the high scaffolding that she was standing on. She laughs and says, *"It's just like taking chemo."* You destroy what you have and then build it back up. When she was diagnosed, she began to research her enemy and planned her attack. She won.

Kathy Slusher

"Don't let fear paralyze you."

When she was diagnosed with breast cancer, Annie says, *"I didn't cry then, and I've never cried. I guess I am like Bob Hope—full of fun!"* When asked what made her a survivor, she says, *"You know you got it. You know something's got to be done. Just go on and do it. It's just like being pregnant. That baby's gonna come one day sooner or later. No need to lay down and holler. Let that baby come on. It's just life."*

Annie Tate

"Just because we've got cancer, that don't mean we got to die with it."

Marilyn was terrified when she was diagnosed with cancer. *"A few months before, I lost my best friend to breast cancer. I sat with her the entire time she was sick. Cindy was forty-two."* It was Cindy who reminded Marilyn to do a self-exam. After a double mastectomy, chemo, and radiation, Marilyn organized a breast cancer support group. In 1994, the American Cancer Society gave Marilyn a statewide Lifesaver Award. But, she says, her best reward came from her son. When an injury forced him to give up football, a sport he loved, and find another goal in life, he told his mother, *"I've watched you. I know I'll make it because I've seen your strength."*

Marilyn Tillery

"It's going to be okay. We'll walk through this together."

In 1981 Anne's doctor told her she had cancer. He advised her to go home and prepare her family for her death. She had three small children, and she had just been widowed the month before. Anne says she might have given up if she hadn't met the Reach to Recovery volunteers. Fourteen years later, Anne is a longtime member of this group and makes her rounds at the hospital every week. Her work enables women to feel hope. Anne laughs as she says, *"I still get a Christmas card from my doctor. All it says is, 'So, you're still alive.'"*

Anne Voltz

"I lived because my doctor made me mad."

Cancer finally taught her *"to take my own advice,"* says Sharon. For years she has been telling people, *"You can handle this. You can do it. What's inside is the most important. Now I know it's true."* Sharon rises to a challenge by *"doing what you gotta do."* She owns her own boutique, works for the Gardendale City Council, and is wife and mother. Sharon remembers the day that she knew she could not give up. After a hard chemo treatment she was in bed feeling very sick. Her husband came in, looked at her, and said, *"You can't die. You know where everything is."*

Sharon Wade

"It's your life and your breast. Ask your doctors anything you want."

After Joe Ann was diagnosed with cancer she prayed, *"Lord, you made me, you created me, you know everything about me. I cast this problem out and give it to you."* She found her cancer through self-exam. Her diagnosis came so early she had no surgery, only chemotherapy and radiation. Joe Ann reminds us that we are ultimately responsible for our own bodies. *"If you don't feel right about something, pursue it until you do. When I found out I had cancer, I knew it was time to go to work."* She combined good medical care, good attitude, and strong faith to survive. In June 1994 her doctor told her she was free of cancer. *"Hallelujah, thank you, Jesus,"* she cried.

"Keep your head up and your hands in God's hands."

Joe Ann Williamson

Rita has fought hard for her little girls. She has had three miscarriages and one stillborn baby, Hannah Hope. While nursing her third child, she noticed a lump. The doctors said it was too big to be cancer. She insisted on a biopsy. Then she got on her knees. *"You know, Lord, no one will love my children as much as I can. Please let me stay."* As she holds her new little red-haired girl, she is *"overwhelmed with God's mercy."* Rita feels cancer has changed her life. *"I experience utter joy. But the path was paved with difficulty and sorrows. It is a gift to look differently at life, heaven, and my children."*

Rita Wright

"You can't guess what tomorrow will bring. Be here now."

"A diagnosis of breast cancer is not a death sentence. Your life will change. You will have a greater zest for life and a greater capacity to love and be loved."

D.D. Sokol

"She needs you. Help her."

Bruce Sokol

The wind blows and catches D.D.'s hair. Auburn strands, soft as feathers, float free into the air and sail toward the Hudson River. It seems real now—her hair is falling out. Two weeks after the first chemo treatment, D.D. and her husband, Bruce, are on holiday in New York City. Later that day, in the hotel bathroom, D.D. sits and looks in the mirror while Bruce shaves her head. In the reflection, they receive each other's tears—together they are preparing for battle. Arm in arm, husband and wife advance to the front line, ready for victory.

D.D. Sokol